WHAT GIVES US
OUR NAMES

BABETTE'S FEAST
III

WHAT GIVES US OUR NAMES

by

ALVIN PANG

MATH PAPER PRESS

FIFTH EDITION, 2016

MATH PAPER PRESS by BOOKSACTUALLY

www.booksactually.com/mathpaperpress.html

———

SERIES DIRECTION by LAO FU ZI

ART DIRECTION by SARAH AND SCHOOLING

PRINTED IN SINGAPORE BY MARKONO PRINT MEDIA PTE LTD

ISBN 978-981-07-0128-4

"Truly," he said, *"it is what we love that gives us our names."*

COMMUNITY

▬

IT WAS a special birthday, so many friends and well wishers gathered to mark the occasion. Service and Commitment were first on the scene to get everything ready. Generosity took care of the catering. Inspiration provided music. Patience said she'd clean up afterwards, and Persistence made sure everyone was notified about the party. The room they were in was just the right temperature, and decked with colourful balloons, wonderful toys and intriguing books, kindly supplied by Memory.

Soon Compassion arrived, bearing flowers and those deep questions of hers that both demonstrated and paved the way for love. Clarity brought candles, videos, and the necessary hush so everyone could be heard. Many old friends got reacquainted, awkwardly at first and then with greater warmth. Purpose embraced Joy, who brought her two children: Daring and Dreaming. Regret caught up with Learning and Maturity. Imagination and Discipline promised to keep in touch more often. And when the old photos, stories and jokes were shared around, even Duty and Pride could not help but laugh.

Presently, everyone noticed their host in the room, looking as rosy as ever and none the worse for his age except a few strands of grey and a slight paunch. A fine mentor, he had taught everyone the difference between "I" and "We", and how "Them" becomes "Us". Then all the gathered friends sat in a circle, raised their glasses and toasted the one whose presence, sympathy and quiet advice had meant so much over the years: the one they all knew as Community.

SUCCESS

Success is buying another condo next week. He already has one for himself, and one for his parents, so this new apartment, he says, is for investment purposes. He's just bought a car to satisfy Progress and Insecurity, his parents, whom he tells me will want to go for another round-the-world vacation very soon. He's also bought a sports car for himself, which he's thinking of changing again because it doesn't go fast enough for him.

We're in a café in the business district, where Success occupies a top-floor office in a prominent corporate tower. Success is well-dressed as usual, but his hair is greying early. When he talks, his eyes tend to look around, as if spotting someone he knows who's just come in. Sometimes, he has a distant look, as if gazing deep into the horizon. Those who don't know him attribute it to his arrogance and indifference. Those who do know him understand that he listens deeply, and is trying to connect what he knows with what he has just heard, in order to learn something new. He is always looking ahead.

Success has always been good at numbers and appearances. Years ago, when we were together in college, he was the sort everyone wanted to have around all the time.

Back then, he was pursuing Purpose, and they did seem a perfect couple to those who knew them both. Since then however, they have not seen much of each other, except at other people's weddings. After that, Purpose went abroad in search of her beloved Passion, who has been missing for a while now. Success immersed himself in work, and eventually met and married Complacency, who is easy to please. He still hasn't forgotten his first love, and hopes that their paths would cross again. In fact, I suspect he's been secretly trying to track her down all this time. He won't admit this, of course—he's afraid of what he might do and what he would have to give up, if he really found Purpose again.

BEAUTY

Beauty must have been just about everywhere. I've seen the mark she leaves wherever she goes. You can see it in the smiling faces of young men, the misty nostalgia of the old. Beauty is much sought after, and very much missed. Poets write her long, pleading letters disguised as verse. Artists try to sketch her portrait, hoping someone who has seen her recently would know where she might be. Somehow, children have the least trouble remembering where she's last been.

It's not that Beauty is aloof, or deliberately elusive. Beauty had been a child star, when her fresh innocence and infectious laughter had charmed multitides. Her parents told her not to go outdoors too much. They were afraid of what dangers the world might pose. So she hid herself where only a few privileged admirers could find her. Sculptors and scholars, artists and millionaires would come to woo her. At first, it was all very exciting, even flattering. But Beauty soon grew tired of being treated like an exhibit or a possession. One night, when no one was looking, she ran away. They've been searching for her ever since. The authorities have no idea where to start. All the clues given by those who claim to know her have led to dead ends.

You'd have thought that Beauty would've been recognised by now. Perhaps she has always been good at hiding in plain sight. She can walk down a busy street and not be noticed by a single passer-by. Then again, most of them have their heads down all the time, and are usually in a hurry. Or maybe no one expects to see Beauty appearing around their ordinary neighbourhood, so it doesn't sink in even when she's right in front of them, or just across the street.

Beauty has had many lovers. She's been known to visit some of her old companions, Passion, Truth, and Joy quite frequently, but she enjoys the company of anyone who will spend some time with her, and not make too much of a fuss about it. Some would say she is pretty indiscriminate who she hangs out with. Once in a while, someone who knows her will run into her, quite by accident. Occasionally, you'll hear someone declaring that he's pinned her down at last. But the moment too much attention is drawn, Beauty disappears again.

Sometimes I think I catch glimpses of Beauty, usually in the oddest of places—at some small art gallery, in between old shop-houses, in the swaying branches of a raintree, a stone's throw away from sunset, in the shadow of cracked paint. You might have seen her yourself—she's small for her age, but very nimble, shy yet insatiably curious. She has an inner glow which makes it seem like she lights up the air around her. Just once, I managed to look into her eyes— they were bright and sad and lonely, and so shiny I could see my reflection in them. From that moment, I lost all desire to hunt her down. She could be anywhere by now.

If you do spot Beauty, take some time to get to know her. She will not stay. but she may rest for a while and tell you the stories she's picked up from her years on the road. Beauty has a soft, soft voice—most people would miss what she has to say, unless they were really paying attention. But if you listen carefully, you might learn where to find Beauty again the next time you need her in your life.

RACE

———

Race was naive enough to think that dyeing her hair was enough to alter the pigment of her name, the nature of her shadow. She tried lime green to generate more zest; a fiery red to suggest deep-seated passions; even black, for that laid-back retro look. But nothing changed. People walked past her on the street, eyes averted, clasping their gaudy shopping-bags watchfully. In school she sat in the corner, hoping to blend in with the cracked paint. Her lovers continued to call her by other names when making love. In the dark, and in the throes of ecstasy, they claimed, everyone looked the same. It was easy to be confused. Race was not convinced. She felt different inside, a place where the moonlight could not reach. She tried using a microscope, a DNA test, her rose-tinted glasses, but could not figure out why the softly pulsing engine of her being remained invisible to her. Did she not have a name? A history? And did she not buy her own clothes with money she earned the same way as everyone else? Disappointed, Race realised that her soul was not the sum of her choices, nor her genes a composite of caresses and strokes leading up to her conception. She envied her friends, the purity of their obliviousness, how they wore their hair casually long and streaked with gold, gleaming against their skin, beneath which the blood coursed, without question, like a final answer. She wondered if she peeled back their flesh, unhinged the bone, eased apart the knotted sinews, whether she would also find nothingness there: a space worn away in the shape of their own silences; what colour it must be.

PASSION

▬

We've not seen Passion for some time now. Some say that he's gone into hiding, others say he's living in another country, and still others say he's being detained without trial, although no-one knows quite what he's done to warrant this. His absence has raised many eyebrows and quite a few questions. Passion would have liked that. Even back in school when we first knew him, he was always asking awkward questions— the important ones with no easy answers. He dreamed of becoming a public prosecutor for a while, just so he could make people admit what they were really up to, and why.

We used to have Passion stay over on weekends and during vacations, or when we had something that needed to be done. He was good with projects, excellent with his hands, and brilliant at coming up with unexpected solutions to pressing problems. But he could never wait for things to happen. Back when we were children together, adults used to say that he had poor manners, was brash and worse, naïve. Passion never listened. He would keep his folks awake at night, tinkering away in the basement workshop, or spending the night in the study.

For as long as I've know him, Passion has been a poor house guest. He has no qualms about dropping in at the most inconvenient times, interrupting whatever I am doing, and demanding that I listen to what he has to say. He is obstinate, often tactless, ruthlessly uncompromising, even when he's being put up with, and hates to be patronised—all of which may explain why he gets into trouble ever so often.

A few years ago while he was doing some mission work, he met Purpose, and was immediately entranced by her. After Passion got engaged to Purpose, he settled into an even rhythm, and worked harder than ever. That was before we lost sight of him.

The last time I encountered Passion, he had fine features, deep-set eyes, and a certain rough charm which drew some people to him, but put others off. He loved strong colours—night black, angel white, bleeding red, thunderstorm blue. If you come across him, please ask him to drop by. Let him know that we miss him—his smile, his playful seriousness, the way he would take you by the hand and show you what you've always wanted to see.

Passion ⟷ purpose

PURPOSE

Purpose is a clearer thinker than anyone I know. She is also the least forgiving of mistakes, but the most compassionate to those who make them. It all depends on where you're coming from, and whether the error was made from honest ignorance or an attempt to cover things up.

Because she looks quite youthful and is small in stature, Purpose sometimes gets lost in the background at meetings or mass gatherings. But when she stands up to speak, she appears to tower over everyone in the room. Much older people have been known to be intimidated by her stern, unflinching gaze. Her father was Truth, a famous court judge who taught her to put forward her views clearly and firmly. It's stood her in good stead—she is a powerful speaker, an excellent negotiator, and a natural leader. She has never needed glasses.

Purpose is not easy to live with, but she is a loyal friend. The men she used to go out with seldom lived up to her high expectations. They were always the ones who made the first move to leave. She's always had this knack of telling people not what they want to hear, but what they need to know, and this disturbs them.

I can see why Passion and Purpose are so attracted to each other. She's fascinated by his energy and intensity, and he admires her sense of focus, how she can always find her way without making a fuss. She calms and steadies him, and he makes her feel alive.

LEARNING

■

Learning is older than he looks, because he is young at heart. He loves children, and can devote hours to be with them, although they often forget about their time together when they grow up. This saddens him somewhat, although he never fails to watch them from behind the scenes in case they need help. Then he steps in and intervenes, often without anyone being aware that he is doing so.

Learning used to work full-time in a school, where he particularly enjoyed small-group teaching, lab work and extra-curricular activities. He would often spend hours after class with students, talking about things outside the syllabus, such as the meaning of life, the value of relationships, and how to comfort the dying. He's acquired quite a reputation— companies now regularly hire him as a consultant, and grown men are turning to him for advice. He's quite pleased about his new work, and it keeps him busy.

An incorrigible traveller, Learning enjoys solitude, but is not addicted to it. I've bumped into him on vacation many times, travelling alone. When he goes abroad, he brings along very little, although he's comfortably endowed. Patient, resourceful and insatiably curious, he trusts the journey to provide whatever he needs.

You don't need to have known Learning for very long to understand that he's a perpetual optimist. Those who know his father, Experience, say that Learning takes after him. What they often overlook is that Reflection was the mother of Learning, and that his favourite teacher is Joy.

ANXIETY

———

I used to run into Anxiety a lot back when I was rushing from place to place. She would always want me to sit down with her and talk, but then refuse to tell me anything much. She once woke me up in the middle of the night, and all I could listen to was the sound of her breathing. I spent a lot of time with her in cafes, until I realized that she was addicted to caffeine and the sound of her own voice.

Anxiety craves attention. She loves bringing people bad news. At meetings, she used to shut people up when they were about to say something interesting. In a crisis, she would be the loudest voice in the room. She is difficult to ignore, and has always been a poor listener. Until I learnt to step away from her, I never knew the quality of my own voice.

It's unclear why I ever spent so much time with her. Perhaps I was fascinated by her loneliness, or was in love with her presence. I remember her as always being hungry, constantly gnawing at anything she could lay her hands on. She has grown so large and awkward, that she is afraid to go out and meet people. She might spend hours dressing up, but no matter what she wears, she feels naked in front of others. She has forgotten how to laugh.

Nowadays she stays mostly indoors, talking to Despair, who is blind. She feels heavy and lethargic, and keeps the curtains drawn so people outside cannot see how gross she has become. Still, even though Anxiety claims to prefer the dark, I know she has a secret pair of wings which she's forgotten how to use. Deep in her heart, what she truly wants is to fly again—if only she could be sure of never falling.

Anxiety — Despair.

falling ...

FREEDOM

—

Freedom wears her hair in extraordinary braids. Her dark eyes flash with a life none of us have truly seen. She spent some years in the field as a soldier, where she fought alongside other men and women for the same fierce cause. After the fighting Freedom and her comrades were asked to put down their weapons and wait to be called to work. But Freedom was restless, and deeply suspicious of those in power. She walked into the bush again, and started a farm with her own hands. Years later she would teach others too how to plant sweat and reap selves.

People came from far away to learn her song, but she would only take the ones who already knew how to sing it by heart. Take this, she would say to them. Play your music to the weary and the lost. Show them how to listen to the land, the wind, the voices of unborn children. Many turned away, puzzled and disappointed, but some heeded her words and became great teachers and mothers.

The books Freedom writes are stories of her many lives, the wisdom of the road and the beauty of motion. They are all for her son, whose name is Tomorrow.

FAILURE

Failure was not an attractive child. When he was born, even his parents were disappointed. They had wanted a beautiful, bonny, dimpled child, like their firstborn, Achievement. Instead, Failure had come into the world a small, lethargic, grey-skinned baby who seldom smiled. Relatives who came to visit tried not to look at him too much. They huddled in corners, whispering and shaking their heads.

Failure had a lonely childhood. At school, Failure was a good student who learnt much and in fact had lots to share. He kept asking questions on subjects that were not in the textbook, and trying things that were not part of the lesson. His teachers thought he was a troublemaker. Most of the other students shunned him. He began to acquire a reputation for being odd, as well as ugly, and began keeping to himself.

Later on, at work, Failure tried to make himself useful. He involved himself in as many things as possible. He attempted to spearhead new projects, trying out new ideas that no one in the organisation had thought of before, but soon found that there were few others who were willing to chip in. Before long, he was burnt out with running around. When things went wrong, fingers were pointed at him, even though he was often the first to discover the problem in the first place. Eventually, he lost his job.

It was while he was setting up his own business that he met Humility. She was a teacher in the school he once attended, helping students with difficulties, and wanted a non-conventional role model to inspire them. His name and student record had caught her eye, and she wrote him a beautiful letter inviting him to speak to some of her students. Failure was more than surprised, but quickly agreed. He spent many months with Humility and her students. With Humility's help, he found at last a willing audience for the lessons his experiences had taught him. Within the year, they were married.

That was some years ago, before his business took off. He had many false starts, but Humility was always with him, and many of their former students became staunch supporters of his work, and themselves went on to break new ground in their fields. When asked, they always cited Failure's lessons those many years ago as being the most important element behind their successes. I hear they're now thinking of starting up a foundation in his name.

As for Failure and Humility, they had two children

who look nothing like their parents, but who share their deep strength of spirit. Much sought after these days, they are known as Experience and Wisdom. Ask them and they will tell you the story of your life.

DESPAIR

■

Despair asks only one thing—that you give yourself up to his care. After travelling a long, hard and dusty road, it is tempting to step aside and into his shade, where he serves a light tea of milk and tears, and wafers baked with sighs. He will tell you, among other tales, how he came to be in this quiet place, off the main thoroughfare, after deciding, midway through some forgotten and risky venture, that it was more prudent to stay put, settle and set up shop. Many of his customers have been there all their lives.

Despair keeps no clocks. If you ask him the time, he will always say it is too late to complete your journey. He will tell you his is the last stop there is, anywhere. Do not trust the wily old shopkeeper. Instead, rest a while and thank him for his stories of lost glory. Then it is best to be on your way.

SERVICE

——

Work is love made visible. - Kahlil Gibran

It is difficult for Service to stand out. Many people do the same work as she, and there are few opportunities to be noticed for excellence. Only when things go wrong are fingers pointed at her. This happens every once in a while, because she has many responsibilities and answers to more than one master. Despite this, she keeps doing more than what Efficiency decrees or Duty expects. This puzzles her bosses completely.

Her habit of doing what is most needed, instead of what is asked of her, attracts many critics and suspicions. But her followers appreciate the free hand they enjoy when working for her, and her firm but clear advice when guidance is needed. Service is an excellent teacher, who never asks more than anyone is able to give, and often shows people how much more they are capable of than they have ever imagined. Her own mentor, Purpose, once told her to always remember that she is the most important person in her field—the one who is there at the time.

When asked to describe her job, Service says she is an artist. This frequently raises eyebrows and much laughter.

"What creative genius can there be in your work?" is the inevitable question. To which she would reply with patience and good humour: "That is my art—to find it, every day."

HOPE

███

for Laleh and Ladan Bijani

Hope was exhausted, worn-out, frayed. Over the years, her vision—once the brightest and clearest there was—had become clouded with fatigue and worry over the thousands little chores needed to take care of her many clients daily.

She was called on all the time, for every reason imaginable—to watch over the smallest of promises, to end an unnecessary silence, or gift a child with things he did not truly require. She answered so many requests that people started to notice only when she failed to show, or even when she was merely late for a much anticipated appointment. She received many complaints and drop-outs.

The past few years, fraught with war and pestilence and tragedy, had not been good for her—the work load had mounted, but her resources had dwindled also. Even among her hard-working staff, there were those who faltered: the pattern was clear enough—beginning among the most fervent of her crew, they burnt out with waiting; resignation soon followed and they were quickly lost to her rivals.

Most of the time, she tried her best to do what she could, even for those deeply skeptical of her abilities. Her most innovative solutions also tended to be her quietest and most subtle, and as a result, she found it difficult to raise support for her causes despite her successes—unlike her competitors, Anger and Delight, who have never been more powerful.

And then she came across the case of two sisters, who wanted nothing else than simply to be apart; who longed—as hard as true lovers yearned to be joined—to hold each other at arm's length, look into each other's faces and laugh. They had travelled a long way to see her, and with a certainty possessed by too few of those who'd come asking for her favours.

When Hope told them how little she could do under the circumstances, expecting them to turn away in dismay and leave, she was surprised to find them smiling at her, their trembling hands locked to hers in the shape of a plea.

With eyes made keen again by tears she set them free of each other, let them bid their farewells and walk at last apart, on their final and separate journeys across the endless fields.

COURAGE

———

"The 76-year-old professor and Holocaust survivor blocked the door to his classroom with his body so students could escape the gunman by jumping out windows."

In memory of Liviu Librescu and other victims of the Virginia Tech shootings, 16 April 2007.

Courage might be the last person you'd go to for answers these days. Unassuming, frail-looking and sometimes distracted, he seems to lack the glamour and forcefulness of Action, the casual brilliance of Talent, or the wisdom and prudence of Caution. His students, who graduate and go on to find Success, hardly ever give him a second thought. But they forget how they first sought Courage when looking for direction in their lives, beginning new endeavours, or falling in love. Those who felt stuck only had to speak with Courage to find themselves already making a first step towards progress.

In fact, Courage enjoys being out of the limelight. He has never hesitated to do the right thing, even in private, nor does he fuss about being given credit. He has pioneered many new ideas and techniques, largely when no one was paying him any attention, and he could work at them with Focus and Patience, his most reliable colleagues. Only he could comfort Anxiety, with gentle kisses and quiet jokes that drew her away from her own self absorption. Courage loves running marathons; what he lacks in energy and brawn, he makes up for in spirit and persistence.

No one really knows where Courage came from or who his parents were. In his youth, he was considered a hero, and many things, good and evil, have been done in his name. But he prefers to be remembered for his garden— where even the tiniest seeds brave the wind and rain, he says, because it is their nature to grow or die.

I once asked Courage what he was afraid of. He joked that he lived every day in fear that it would be his last. And then as I turned to go, he whispered to me what he truly feared above all else: that things would remain only as they are.

COMPLEXITY

████

There are few who would genuinely recognise Complexity if she showed up; and yet many claim to know her intimately. It's true that Complexity has a reputation for being exotic and elusive, and those who become familiar with her sometimes make their fortune. However, she has also been snubbed for being too flamboyant, unpredictable and more than a little difficult to manage. She is not known to be tidy.

Some fear that Complexity might be a disruptive influence on the impressionable or the ill-prepared. The common perception is that she leaves a trail of chaos in her wake, and she is said to have been spotted often around warzones, boardrooms and markets. It certainly seems that her voice is loudest in a mob, even though it isn't always clear what she has to say until much later and in quieter moments.

Although Complexity does visit dizzying, glamorous places, from the inner orbits of atoms to Alpha Centauri, you might run into her just about anywhere. Complexity also frequents the most ordinary of habitats: beaches, anthills, kindergartens, clouds, the dreams of harried mothers. Curiosity and Wonder—friends who know her well—suggest that she tends to be so involved in whatever she is doing that sometimes she disappears from sight. Then Complexity can remain invisible or appear drab and ordinary for years before bursting again onto the scene. Somehow, we always manage to be caught unawares.

You can tell the resemblance between Complexity and her twin brother, Truth. While they have very different personalities, both are concerned with things as they are, not as we might wish them to be. While Truth commands the respect of great men and high-minded leaders, Complexity demonstrates that even the smallest actions can shape the future. It is a matter of seeing how one thing connects with another, in ways that we might not have realised.

Complexity is exhausting to be around. It is not as if she offers stability, comfort, quick answers or the certainty of progress. Of all who have courted her over the years, only Vision manages to keep up with her restlessness. In her presence, he has come to appreciate the value of difference, and the gift of surprise. Walking through her Garden of the New, he learns how simple rules can lead to the most dramatic and unexpected outcomes. Every seed carries within it the dream and blueprint of the whole.

Despite Complexity's many demands, Vision embraces her fully. For as long as she exists, the world will never want for mystery.

PATIENCE

——

At 9 he planted a clutch of seed blooms, carefully observed their daily frenzy.

At 22 he began documenting the story of the river which ran behind his house, down from the foothills of a nearby mountain and on to the distant ocean. It told him everything he asked of it, and more, eagerly and without pause, until the winter months, when it finally withdrew, spent and drymouthed, to the mountains to sleep.

It was then that he would write down all that he'd heard, in long cursive script that meandered across the page. He had time; he was alone, and the fire was well-fed with wood from the surrounding forests, whose tale he also recorded, when he was 30.

At 46 he started a biography of the wind, who'd often peaked over his shoulder while he worked by the water's edge; not until he was 54 did he catch her often enough to probe and grasp her deeper impulses.

By the time he turned 63 he was ready to begin his memoirs. It was of course going to be his most difficult work. People lived so fiercely, he remarked once, often as if they could cease to be at any moment, and at other times, as if they were going to be around forever.

No one knows what happened to the final manuscript. Critics who had seen his work in progress described it as a chronicle of history through the eyes of the forgotten. By now he had many imitators as well as detractors, many of whom were once admirers who gave up waiting for him to complete each work.

Years after his death at the age of 110, someone at long last recognised his true magnum opus: a carefully pruned pattern of ash, dew, footsteps and flowering trees in the shape of a single haiku, imprinted on the land where he used to live, and visible only from the heavens.

CONGRUENCE

It had not been an easy journey for Congruence. He had set forth with grand ambitions, lofty ideals and many followers, but it wasn't long before companions left him, appalled by the uncertain demands of the road.

His robes, once a pristine satin white, were now sullied and worn from the effort of travel. He'd had to endure the public heat of day, unexpected storms, dense fog, treacherous quagmires; and sudden tricky hills he did not know how to climb, except one slow step at a time, trying not to slip.

It was seldom clear what his next milestone would be. Many times he stumbled over unseen crevices in the dark, without even the mercy of moonlight to guide him. And always there were things to be taken care of: shelter, the next meal, the safety of his wife and child. But not once did he think of turning back.

To survive, he learnt how to swim, to speak plainly, to move quickly when necessary, to wait and to rest. He developed a deep distaste for masks and a healthy respect for mirrors. But he was always kind to those who seemed lost or afraid to cross the desert. By leading the way, he showed them how to keep moving forward and to navigate by their own stars.

At a toll-booth he was detained by Doubt, who demanded proof that he knew where he was going; and whether he had sufficient funds or a return ticket. Emptying his pockets, Congruence displayed the wealth of stories and spare tears he had earned along the way, and pointed in the direction of the future.

This was how, at last, Congruence arrived at the feast. It did not matter that he was dusty and bruised from his voyage, nor that other guests had already taken their places. With open arms they welcomed him and listened in awe as he described landscapes and heartlands that no one else before had walked or witnessed. He spoke of how in his darkest moments when the path seemed lost, the clear song of his wife, Conviction, had kept him from wandering astray.

"Truly," he said, "it is what we love that gives us our names."

Then their son Integrity—who had started the journey as an infant and was now a grown man—stepped forward proudly and began to sing.

―

ABOUT THE AUTHOR

—

ALVIN PANG has been known to edit, explore, curate, comment, read, review, photograph, perform, translate, travel, teach, dine, document, design, dream and adore cats. Generous spirits from many shores have feted his words in fellowships, feasts and festivities. Translators in over a dozen languages have puzzled over his poetry. He aspires to elusiveness, accepts that life is brief and considers restlessness a virtue. He has always needed glasses.

ABOUT THE TYPE

▬

THIS TEXT USES the type Hoefler Text, which is a contemporary serif Antiqua font that was designed for Apple Computer to demonstrate advanced type technologies.

Hoefler Text was created to allow the composition of complex typography; it takes cues from a range of classic fonts, such as Garamond and Janson.

BABETTE'S FEAST

———

BABETTE'S FEAST[1] is a fortnightly public gathering of writers, initiated and organised by *BooksActually*, where a diversity of writers—writers of singular words, writers of sentences, writers of letters, writers of lyrics, writers of stories, writers of fact, writers of the ephemeral—come together to share their written works in the midst of earnest company, warm conversation and a humble feast. This series of chapbooks are borne from these sessions.

———

[1] BABETTE'S FEAST has its origins from Isak Dinesen's short story of the same title — an enchanting celebration of feasting, company and gratitude.

MATH PAPER PRESS

———

Math Paper Press

MATH PAPER PRESS, an imprint of *BooksActually*, is a small press publisher of poetry, new wave novellas, short story anthologies, full-length novels and essays. Its eclectic range of literary and visual works also includes photography collections, memoirs and young adult fiction. Math Paper Press also distributes books by selected small presses.